Really Easy Guitar!

Contents

This book © Copyright 2003 by Wise Publications
8/9 Frith Street, London W1D 3JB

Unauthorised reproduction of any part of this publication by any means including photocopying is an infringement ofcopyright.

Written and arranged by Cliff Douse
Music processed by Simon Troup
Edited by Sorcha Armstrong and Tom Fleming
Book design by Chloë Alexander
Cover and book photographs courtesy of London Features International
Introduction photographs by George Taylor
Printed in the United Kingdom

CD mastered by Jonas Persson
Guitars by Arthur Dick

Got any comments?
e-mail reallyeasyguitar@musicsales.co.uk

Introduction

Welcome to *Really Easy Guitar! Riffs*. If you've used *Really Easy Guitar!* before, you'll know that we usually supply a riff for each song in the book. Here, we've put together 42 of the best riffs of all time into one book!

We've made it even easier by recording every riff slowly without backing band, so you can hear exactly what's going on in the guitar part.

Follow the demonstration along with the music and tab, practise it yourself a few times until you feel confident, then try playing along with the full-speed 'soundalike' version!

The CD track numbers in the book refer to the slowed down recording of each riff. The backing track version is always the next track.

1 Tune Your Guitar

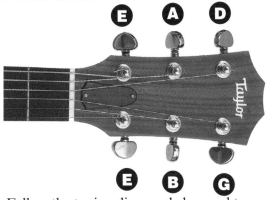

Before you can start to play along with the riffs, you'll need to make sure that your guitar is in tune with the CD. Track 1 on the CD gives you notes to tune to for each string, starting with the top E string, and then working downwards.

Alternatively, tune the bottom string first and then tune all the other strings to it.

Follow the tuning diagram below and tune from the bottom string upwards.

6th to 5th string	5th to 4th string	4th to 3rd string	3rd to 2nd string	2nd to 1st string

2 Understanding fretbox diagrams

Throughout this book, fretbox diagrams are used to show chord shapes and scale patterns. Think of the box as a view of the fretboard from head on – the thickest (lowest) string is on the left and the thinnest (highest) string is on the right.

The horizontal lines correspond to the frets on your guitar; the circles indicate where you should place your fingers.

An **x** above the box indicates that that string should not be played; an **o** indicates that the string should be played open.

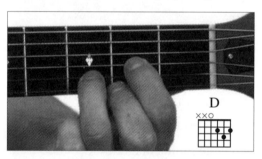

D
xxo

If the riff is chord-based, the chords you will need are given above each riff.

Shapes that are played higher up the neck are described in the same way – the lowest fret used is indicated to the right of the box. A curved line above the box shows that a first finger barre should be used.

G
3fr

This barre chord of G is played at the third fret, with the first finger stretching across all six strings.

3 Understanding scale patterns

We can also use chord box diagrams to show you certain useful scale patterns on the fretboard. When a box is used to describe a scale pattern, suggested fingerings are also included.

Black circles show you the root note of the scale. If the root note of the scale is an open string, this is indicated by a double circle. Grey circles represent notes of the scale below the lowest root note.

So in this example, the root note of the scale is the open D string, with another D appearing at the third fret on the B string.

4 Understanding TAB

TAB is another easy way to learn the famous riffs and hooks in each song. The six horizontal lines represent the six strings of the guitar – the lowest line represents the lowest string (low E), while the highest line represents the highest string (high E). The number on each line tells you which fret should be played.

Although we've also included traditional music notation, you don't actually need to be able to read music to use TAB – just listen to the recording and follow the fret positions on the TAB and you'll soon be playing along. There are certain special symbols which are used:

Hammer-on

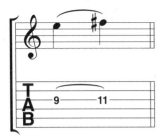

Look out for a slur connecting two numbers – when the second number is higher than the first this is called a "hammer-on". Place one finger at the lower of the two frets indicated and pick that string, then, without picking the string again, place your next finger at the higher fret. You should hear a smooth change in sound between the two notes.

Pull-off

A Pull-off is the opposite of a hammer-on, and is denoted by a slur joining two TAB numbers, where the second number is lower than the first one.

Place your fingers at the two fret positions indicated, and pick the first (higher) note, then simply lift the top finger, without picking the string again, allowing the bottom note to ring out.

Slide

A slide between two notes is denoted by a short line in the TAB. Simply play the first note, and then move your finger to the new fret position by sliding it along the fretboard, restriking the string as you arrive at the new position.

Legato slide

A legato slide is exactly the same as a normal slide, except that the second note is not picked again.

Bend

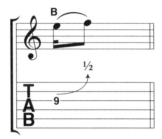

String bends are indicated as shown above – the amount that you need to bend the string is indicated near the arrow and could be $1/4$ one (a decorative bend), $1/2$ tone (the equivalent of one fret) or full (the equivalent of two frets).

Palm Muting

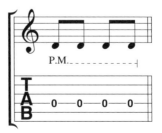

To get this percussive effect, place the side of your picking hand against the strings near the bridge as you pick.

2 All Day And All Of The Night

The Kinks | Release date: October 1964 | Chart position: 2 | Album: *Kinks*

ALTHOUGH THEY WEREN'T AS innovative or popular as the Beatles or Rolling Stones, the Kinks were still one of the most influential pop bands of the Sixties. Like many bands from that era, the Kinks began as an R&B act, but they developed a distinctly 'British' sound by the end of the decade.

How to play it

Position your first finger behind the 1st fret on the 6th string and use your second finger to barre the notes behind the 3rd fret on the 4th and 5th strings. This is your first chord – F5.

To play the other two chords, G5 and B♭5, simply move the whole chord shape two frets and five frets up the fingerboard respectively from your original position (your first finger moves to the 3rd fret for the G5 chord and the 6th fret for the B♭5 chord).

Guitar sound

This riff works well with any solidbody or semi-solid electric guitar. Use the bridge pickup and put it through an amp with a hint of distortion and plenty of reverb.

"Dave would do anything to get a dirtier sound. He'd kick the amp every now and then."
Shel Talmy, The Kinks' producer

The most authentic Kinks rhythm guitar sound can be obtained by using an amp equipped with a spring reverb.

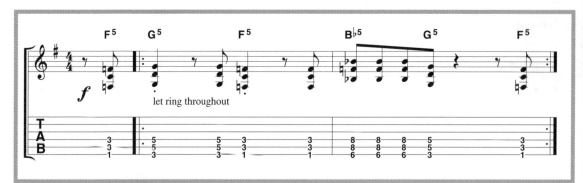

let ring throughout

Words & Music by Ray Davies
© Copyright 1964 Edward Kassner Music Company Limited.
All Rights Reserved. International Copyright Secured.

4 Sunshine Of Your Love

Cream | Release date: October 1968 | Chart position: 25 | Album: *Disraeli Gears*

'SUNSHINE OF YOUR LOVE' BOASTS one of Cream's most popular and enduring motifs – a grinding Clapton guitar riff which propels the song. This riff paved the way for early heavy metal bands like Led Zeppelin, Black Sabbath and Deep Purple.

How to play it

This famous Cream riff starts off with D and C chords based on the barred E major shape, followed by a bluesy line on the 5th and 6th strings.

The second play of the riff starts off the same way but ends on a higher note. In both cases, add some vibrato to the last note to add extra colour and dynamics.

Guitar sound

Clapton used a psychedelic Gibson SG guitar for this riff. He rolled the tone control of the neck pickup back to zero and played through an overdriven Marshall. You too can get this guitar sound by playing a solidbody guitar with humbucker pickups through a rock amp with overdrive.

"[The riff] was strictly a dedication to Jimi. And then we wrote a song on top of it."
Eric Clapton

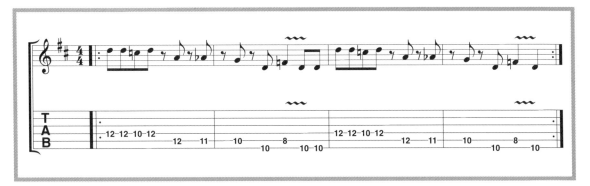

6 Oye Como Va

Santana | Release date: September 1970 (album track) | Album: *Abraxas*

CARLOS SANTANA'S UNIQUE BLEND OF blues, rock and latin music has enjoyed a surge in popularity in recent years and he is considered by many to be one of the greatest electric guitar players of all time. His version of Tito Puente's 'Oye Como Va', from the album *Abraxas* (1970), was a pioneering example of latin-rock fusion.

How to play it

Santana's version of Puente's tune is based around two really easy guitar chords: Am7 and D9. The Am7 is played simply by barring your second finger across the first four strings at the 5th fret. The D9 features the 1st, 2nd and 3rd strings barred in the same way by the second finger, along with the note at the 4th fret on the 4th string played by the first finger.

We've tabbed out the melody played on the CD, so you can play either the chord based riff, or the melody.

Guitar sound

Santana has mainly used humbucker-equipped guitars over the years and he played this tune on either a Gibson SG or Les Paul. Use the bridge pickup and play through an amp with a little bit of distortion (but not overdrive) and some reverb.

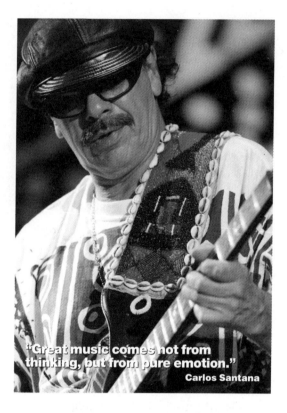

"Great music comes not from thinking, but from pure emotion."
Carlos Santana

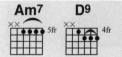

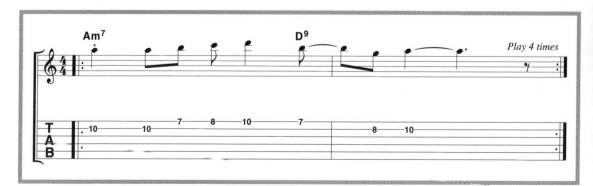

8 Pretty Vacant

Sex Pistols | Release date: July 1977 | Chart position: 6 |
Album: *Never Mind The Bollocks*

THE PISTOL'S NIHILISTIC ATTITUDE
often disguised the fact that they were
actually a tight, robust band. 'Pretty
Vacant' features their most famous intro,
a simple one-chord arpeggio, played before
the power chords and Johnny Rotten's
sneering vocals take over.

How to play it

This easy riff is based around an open A
chord (above). Form the chord and pick
the open 5th string twice. Then pick the 3rd
string twice (one of your fingers is already
holding down at the second fret on this
string to produce the right note). Pick the
open 5th string twice again and then pick
the 4th string twice. Repeat the phrase
again and again, making sure you're using
downstrokes for maximum power.

Guitar sound

Steve Jones, the Pistols' guitarist, favoured
a Gibson Les Paul, but the intro to 'Pretty
Vacant' can be played effectively on
any solidbody guitar going through an
amp with a fair amount of distortion.
Attitude is probably as important as tone
and technique in this instance, so don't

"The Sex Pistols was Punk.
The rest is just merely punk pop,
alright?" John Lydon

forget to practice those sneers as well!

A5

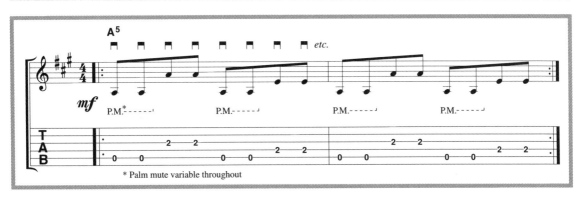

* Palm mute variable throughout

Run To You

Bryan Adams | Release date: January 1985 | Chart position: 11 | Album: *Reckless*

"The mystery of this track is it was recorded with a capo on the second fret, hence the F♯ tuning."
Bryan Adams

BRYAN ADAMS' FIRST UK HIT SINGLE starts with one of the most memorable riffs from the Eighties. Although it might sound a bit tricky to a beginner's ear at first, it is actually based around three easy-to-play chords.

How to play it

If you want to play along with the CD you'll have to use a capo at the second fret. For the first chord, hold down the second fret of the fifth string with your second finger and pick across the 6th, 5th and 4th strings as shown in the music below.

For the second chord, move your third finger over to play the third fret of the sixth string while you continue picking. Then move your fretting fingers up two frets and pick out the remaining five notes. Play this progression repeatedly to obtain the feel of the intro and first verse of the song.

Guitar sound

Bryan is most commonly associated with a Fender Stratocaster guitar, which would be ideal for this intro. Use the middle pickup with only a hint of distortion and, if you can, add a little bit of chorus to smoothen things up.

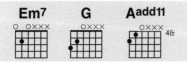

Em7   **G**   **Aadd11**

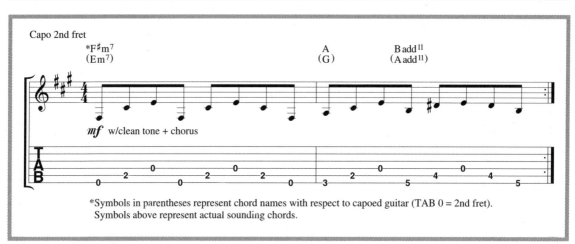

Capo 2nd fret

*F♯m⁷ (Em⁷)   A (G)   B add¹¹ (A add¹¹)

mf w/clean tone + chorus

*Symbols in parentheses represent chord names with respect to capoed guitar (TAB 0 = 2nd fret).
Symbols above represent actual sounding chords.

12 Livin' On A Prayer

Bon Jovi | Release date: October 1986 | Chart position: 4 | Album: *Slippery When Wet*

BON JOVI WERE HUGELY POPULAR during the Eighties and 'Livin' On A Prayer' was their biggest hit in 1986. It features a typical Richie Sambora riff played on the E minor pentatonic scale.

How to play it

The E minor pentatonic scale is easy to play. To get a feel for it, try playing this shape at the 12th fret using diagram shown (left).

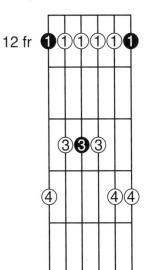

Richie plays the scale using a different part of the neck, combining an open 6th string with fretted notes on the 6th and 5th strings. Play the example slowly at first and then bring it up to speed. Play along with a metronome if you want to build up even greater accuracy.

"I sat at the piano and started messing around with this chord change and it suddenly came to me. When they heard that, everyone was sure it would be a hit!"

Richie Sambora, Bon Jovi

Guitar sound

Sambora is associated with Fender Strats, but you'll find that this riff can be played on just about any electric instrument.

Use an overdriven tone and, if you like, a wah-wah pedal to add a bit of extra colour to the sound.

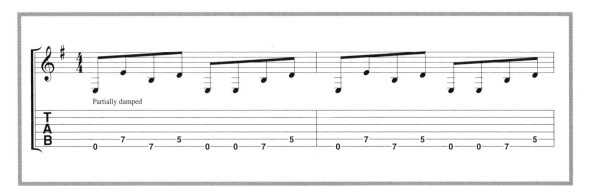

Partially damped

Words & Music by Jon Bon Jovi, Richie Sambora & Desmond Child
© Copyright 1986 PolyGram International Publishing Incorporated/Bon Jovi Publishing/EMI April Music Incorporated/Desmobile Music Company Incorporated, USA.
Universal Music Publishing Limited (66.66%)/EMI Songs Limited (33.34%).
All Rights Reserved. International Copyright Secured.

There She Goes

The La's | Release date: January 1989 (originally) | Chart position: 13 (1990 re-issue)
Album: *The La's*

THIS MUCH LOVED SINGLE received critical acclaim but not commercial success when it was first launched back in the late Eighties. The La's had better luck the second time around after the release of their eponymous debut album in 1990. Drawing from the ringing guitars of mid-Sixties and post-punk bands like the Smiths, their music had an almost timeless feel.

"What keeps us going is memories of the future." Lee Mavers

How to play it

The 'There She Goes' riff is mainly played on the 1st and 2nd strings of the guitar (see below). Start by fretting the note behind the 3rd fret on the 2nd string with your second finger. Let all of the notes ring out, just like they do in the La's version.

Guitar sound

Paul Hemmings and Peter James 'Cammy' Camell played the guitars on this song and their intro has a jangly 12-string Rickenbacker feel to it, reminiscent of Roger McGuinn's sound with the Byrds.

Try this on a 12-string guitar or a regular instrument with a short delay to simulate a 12-string effect.

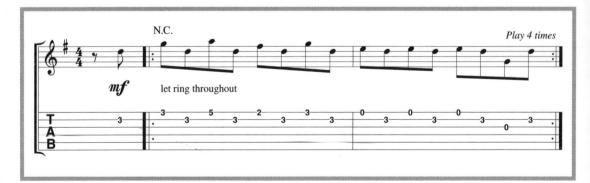

16 Fools Gold

The Stone Roses | Release date: November 1989 | Chart position: 8
Album: *The Stone Roses*

BLENDING SIXTIES-STYLE GUITAR POP
with modern dance beats, the Stone Roses
defined the British guitar pop scene of the
early Nineties and paved the way for bands
like the Charlatans and the Happy
Mondays. 'Fools Gold' marked their
transition from being a 'pubs and clubs'
band to one that played to huge stadium
audiences.

How to play it
Play the first two notes on the 6th and 4th
strings with your 1st and 3rd fingers. Then
play the quick slides from the 5th fret on
the 4th string to the 4th fret and back again
with your first finger (it's easier than it
sounds!), and repeat the approach for the
similar effect on the 5th string.

End up at the 3rd, 4th and 5th frets on
the 6th string with your 2nd, 3rd and 4th
fingers respectively. Practice it slowly at first
before playing along with the CD. Make
sure you mute the appropriate notes, listen
carefully to the CD.

Guitar sound
John Squire, one of the founding members
of the band, played guitar on 'Fools Gold'.
To get the main riff sound, use the bridge
pickup and cut down on your treble with
the guitar's tone control. Use a reasonably
clean sound with just a hint of distortion
and some reverb.

Words & Music by John Squire & Ian Brown
© Copyright 1989 Zomba Music Publishers Limited.
All Rights Reserved. International Copyright Secured.

18 The Day We Caught The Train

Ocean Colour Scene | Release date: June 1996 | Chart position: 4
Album: *Moseley Shoals*

OCEAN COLOUR SCENE WERE championed by Paul Weller and Noel Gallagher, and they went on to become superstars themselves. Their second album, Moseley Shoals, a successful blend of Brit-pop, funk and R&B, spawned this hit single.

How to play it

The chorus of this song is sung over four of the simplest of chords: D, A, G and Em (each played for one bar). These can be played straight or exactly as Steve Cradock played them (as shown in the music examples below).

Guitar sound

Steve Craddock and Simon Fowler used a combination of clean chords and distorted tones in this song. You can get a similar effect by playing the chords through a relatively clean amp setting and stomping on a distortion pedal for the heavier parts.

"One great note is always better than four or five." Damon Minchella

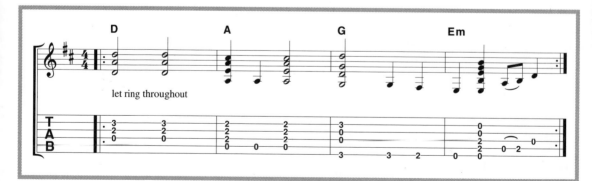

let ring throughout

Words & Music by Steve Cradock, Simon Fowler, Oscar Harrison & Damon Minchella
© Copyright 1995 Island Music Limited. Universal/Island Music Limited.
All Rights Reserved. International Copyright Secured.

20 Road Rage

Catatonia | Release date: May 1998 | Chart position: 5 | Album: *International Velvet*

FALLING SOMEWHERE BETWEEN THE alternative and indie rock camps, Catatonia were one of the most popular bands to emerge out of Wales during the Nineties. The band had two guitar players: Mark Roberts (also a singer) and Owen Powell.

How to play it

You can play all of the song's opening verse chord sequence on the top two strings as shown below. Some of these chord changes might seem like a bit of a jump along the guitar neck at first but they're actually quite easy. Use whichever fingers you feel most comfortable playing with.

Guitar sound

To mimic the rhythm guitar sound used on 'Road Rage', select a middling guitar tone on a solidbody electric and put it through a subtle auto-wah effect with some chorus to smoothen it up.

You can also get this sound on a foot-controlled wah pedal but don't overdo it – unless you want to get seriously funky!

"I sing all the time, you can't shut me up!" Cerys Matthews

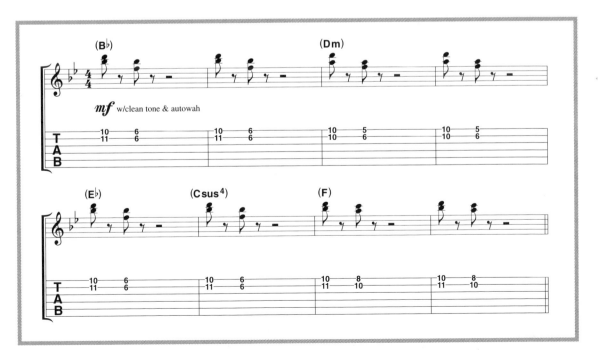

Words & Music by Cerys Matthews, Mark Roberts, Aled Richards, Paul Jones & Owen Powell
© Copyright 1997 Sony/ATV Music Publishing (UK) Limited.
All Rights Reserved. International Copyright Secured.

22 Found That Soul

Manic Street Preachers | Release date: February 2001 | Chart position: 9
Album: *Know Your Enemy*

'FOUND THAT SOUL' IS AN EXCELLENT
example of the raw, energetic rock style
that made the Manic Street Preachers one
of the most popular bands of the Nineties.
The song starts with a riff played by James
Dean Bradfield.

How to play it

Position your first finger by the 9th fret and
play the open 6th string three times. Then
play the C#5 chord as shown below (9th fret
on the 6th string and 11th fret on the 4th
and 5th strings) twelve times and repeat the
whole phrase. Play it all with downstrokes
for optimum power!

Guitar sound

James usually plays this riff on his
trademark white Les Paul, but any guitar
with humbucking pickups should give you
his tone. Use the bridge pickup to obtain
the fattest sound possible and put it
through a heavily overdriven amp with a
dash of reverb.

*"A lot of journalists are saying that
we're irrelevant compared to a lot of
younger bands. I think we're still a
completely aggressive experience.."*
James Dean Bradfield

C#5

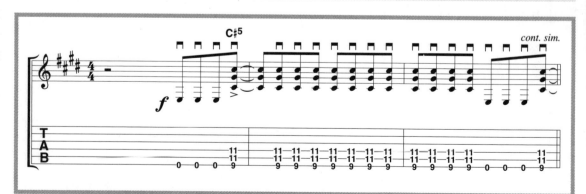

Burn Baby Burn

Ash | Release date: April 2001 | Chart position: 13 | Album: *Free All Angels*

THIS EASY INTRO RIFF WAS PLAYED BY Ash's guitarist, Charlotte Hatherley, on the band's fifth album, and shows the heavy influence of Seventies British rock on the band.

How to play it
Play the two note riff across the 1st and 2nd strings as shown below. It's a little bit too fast for straight downstrokes so you'll have to use alternate picking (alternate down and upstrokes).

Place your first finger behind the 11th fret on the first string, and your second finger behind the 12th fret on the second string, then simply alternate between them. Play the riff slowly at first and then build up to speed – it won't take long!

Guitar sound
Charlotte plays a Gibson SG through a Marshall, but any guitar with humbucking pickups through a rock amp will make this riff sound authentic.

Use the bridge pickup (the one furthest from the neck) with the tone control all the way up, and turn the amp up too!

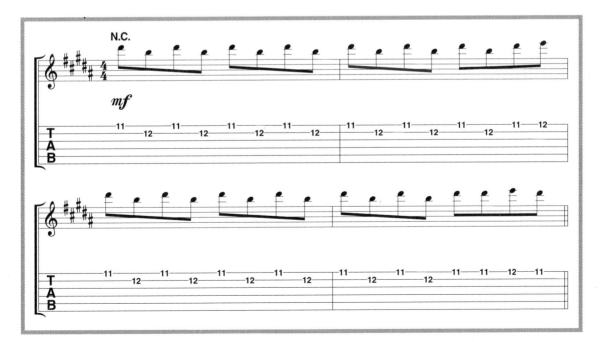

26 Just A Day

Feeder | Release date: December 2001 | Chart position: 12 | From the EP: *Just A Day*

THIS SONG BOASTS ONE OF FEEDER'S most popular riffs. It was released in 2001 with a memorable video showing fans of the band miming along with the song in their bedrooms. Like 'Buck Rogers', it was featured in the PS2 game Gran Turismo 3.

How to play it

Position your fretting hand around the 9th fret on the fingerboard. Hold down the note at the 9th fret on the third (G) string with your first finger and, while keeping it held down, play the note at the 11th fret on the same string with your third finger. Then play the same note again and lift your third finger off to let the note held down by your first finger ring out (it's called a "pull-off" effect), and then play the note at the 9th fret again with your third finger. Repeat the same phrase again but this time finish on the fourth (D) string, at the 9th fret.

Repeat the phrase one more time, just as you first played it, then bend the note at the 11th fret on the third string up with your 3rd finger so that it sounds like the note at the 13th fret on the same string. Stop when you hit that note (don't audibly bend it back down again), play your pull-off effect again, and end on the 11th fret on the fourth string with your third finger. Keep on repeating this sequence of events and you'll nail it in no time!

Guitar sound

Use the bridge pickup on a solidbody electric guitar and put it through an amp with overdrive and a touch of short reverb. You can also increase the amount of distortion, if you want, with a stomp pedal. Careful not to use too much overdrive, though, or you'll end up with a mushy sound!

28 Paranoid

Black Sabbath | Release date: August 1970 | Chart position: 4 | Album: *Paranoid*

BLACK SABBATH'S 'PARANOID' IS ONE of the most influential heavy metal songs of all time. Its bone crushing riffs and Ozzy's manic vocals paved the way for the likes of Judas Priest and Iron Maiden. We're going to look at the intro riff.

How to play it

Barre your first finger across the 5th and 6th strings behind the 12th fret and play both notes together. Then hammer down behind the 14th fret on the 5th string with your third finger. Repeat this three times for the opening phrase. For the second bar, play the note behind the 12th fret on the 5th string with your first finger and hammer down your third finger behind the 14th fret.

Repeat this for the 4th string and then the 5th string again. Finish the riff by playing the note behind the 12th fret on the 4th string with your first finger and then the note behind the 14th fret on the 5th string with your third finger.

Guitar sound

Tony Iommi, Black Sabbath's guitarist, was famous for his monolithic, primal guitar

"In those days, you had to make your own sound, and the band became the sound of what you made."
Tony Iommi

sound. He favoured a Gibson SG and Laney amps. To get an authentic Sabbath sound, get a guitar with humbucking pickups and use the bridge pickup with lots of distortion!

E5

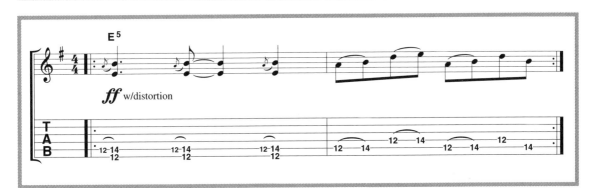

E5

ff w/distortion

30 Highway To Hell

AC/DC | Release date: September 1979 | Chart position: 56 | Album: *Highway To Hell*

THIS CLASSIC RIFF IS A GREAT example of AC/DC's infectious rock at its best: loud, tight and pounding! The song has an eerie resonance today as the band's singer, Bon Scott, an epitome of sex, drugs and rock 'n' roll, died only six months after its release.

How to play it
'Highway To Hell' starts off with a basic A chord, played on the middle four strings: use your first, second and third fingers to hold down the three notes at the second fret. For the next two chords, D/F♯ and G5, hold down the note at the second fret on the third string with your first finger, the note at the third fret on the second string with your second finger, and use your thumb to fret the notes at the second and

third frets on the 6th string. After a couple more of these, the riff finishes on an A chord again.

Guitar sound
Angus Young donned his favourite Gibson SG, along with his essential AC/DC school uniform and satchel, for this number. If you want to get the same kind of sound, you should also use a humbucker equipped guitar – an SG, Les Paul, Flying V or similar – with a rock amp. Use the bridge pickup and turn the overdrive and master volume controls up! (School uniform optional.)

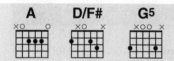

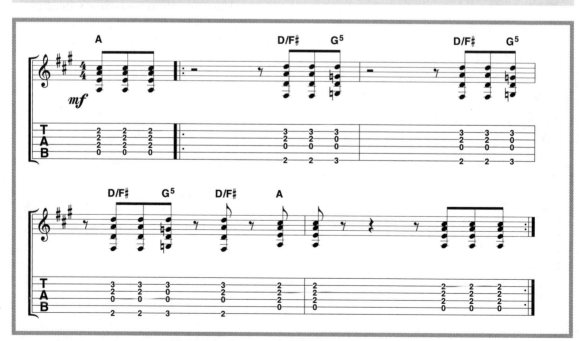

Words & Music by Bon Scott, Angus Young & Malcolm Young
© Copyright 1979 J. Albert & Son Pty. EMI Music Publishing Limited.
All Rights Reserved. International Copyright Secured.

32 Bring Your Daughter... To The Slaughter

Iron Maiden | Release date: January 1991 | Chart position: 1
Album: *No Prayer For The Dying*

EVEN THOUGH THIS CONTROVERSIAL single was banned by the BBC back in 1991, it still reached number one and turned out to be one of Iron Maiden's biggest hits. We're going to take a look at its easy verse guitar riff.

How to play it
Your fretting hand has an easy job for this part: place your first finger behind the second fret on the 4th string and your second finger behind the third fret on the 2nd string.

Now, with your picking hand, pick the fourth, third and second strings to sound an arpeggio (the notes of a chord played individually). Then pick the fifth, fourth and first strings to give the second arpeggio. It's as easy as that!

Guitar sound
Iron Maiden's Janick Gers played a Fender Strat on this song and, unsurprisingly, put it through a Marshall amp. Use the bridge or middle pickup for this example, and turn the amp up loud enough to get the sustain

"I think less is more. Don't try and play a million notes." Dave Murray

needed to make those notes ring out loud and clear.

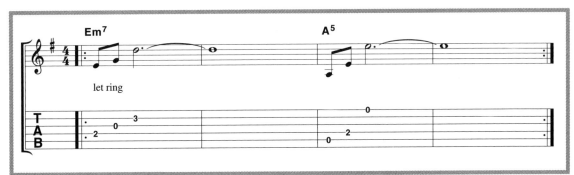

34 Enter Sandman

Metallica | Release date: August 1991 | Chart position: 5 | Album: *Metallica*

'ENTER SANDMAN' WAS RECORDED at a time when Metallica were stripping down the progressive elements of their music to produce a more basic sound. Unlike many heavy metal intros, it starts off with a picked sequence and clean guitar sound.

How to play it

Position your fretting hand with your first finger around the 5th fret and your third finger around the 7th. Play the open 6th string, followed by the note at the 7th fret on the fifth string with your third finger, and then the open 3rd string.

Then play the notes at the 6th and 5th frets on the 6th string with your 2nd and 1st fingers respectively, followed by the 7th fret on the fifth string with your 3rd finger.

Guitar sound

This intro was played with a clean guitar sound to provide a nice contrast with the overdriven tones that kick in afterwards. Use the bridge pickup and select a clean sound with your amp. Add a bit of reverb to give it some extra colour. The sequence also works very well with subtle chorus and flange effects.

"My strength is in writing riffs. I'll never be able to play fast like Kirk." James Hetfield

Falling Away From Me

Korn | Release date: February 2000 | Chart position: 24 | Album: *Issues*

KORN'S UNUSUALLY DARK sound has earned the band a large and loyal following over the past couple of years. Despite this, various areas of the media have branded them as "perverts, psychopaths and paranoiacs".

How to play it

Korn generally use 7-string guitars with dropped tunings but you can easily play this clean intro riff on a normally-tuned 6-string guitar.

Position your fretting hand around the 12th-15th frets and play the notes shown below on the top three strings. Pick the notes out precisely and let them ring out.

Guitar sound

Aim for a relatively clean sound. Korn actually used an electronic vibrato for this passage so you'll need to use one too (or simulate the effect with your fretting fingers) if you want your version to sound just like the original.

"We try to be vulgar without really being vulgar."
James Shaffer

38 Buck Rogers

Feeder | Release date: January 2001 | Chart position: 5 | Album: *Echo Park*

THIS WELL KNOWN FEEDER RIFF WAS used as part of the high octane soundtrack for Sony's popular Playstation 2 game, Gran Turismo 3. It was played by the band's singer and guitarist, Grant Nicholas.

How to play it

The intro riff to 'Buck Rogers' is played on the bottom two strings and is played as straight 8-to-the-bar downstrokes. Position the third finger of your fretting hand behind the 11th fret on the 5th string and play the open 6th string along with this fretted note.

Now move your fretting hand position so that your first finger is behind the 4th fret on the 6th string and your third finger is behind the 6th fret on the 5th string for the second chord of the riff. Finally, move your fretting hand up one fret keeping the same finger position. This riff continues through the first verse and some heavy distortion is added after 8 bars.

Guitar sound

Grant's main guitars are a Fender Jazzmaster solidbody guitar and a Gibson 335 semi-acoustic, but you'll find that you

"I go for a big guitar sound. That's my secret weapon!"
Grant Nicholas

can make this riff sound authentic on almost any electric guitar. Use the bridge pickup (the one furthest away from the neck) through a clean amp setting to produce the basic tone and then stomp on a distortion or overdrive pedal to obtain the heavier version of the riff. It's as simple as that!

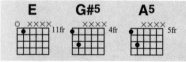

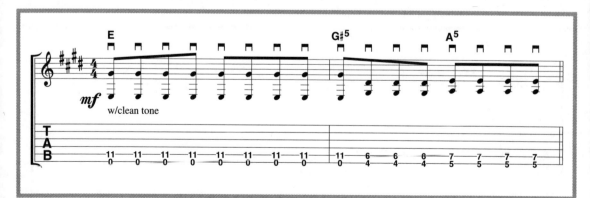

40 Last Resort

Papa Roach | Release date: February 2001 | Chart position: 3 | Album: *Infest*

ALTHOUGH PAPA ROACH FORMED IN Northern California in 1993, they didn't win worldwide recognition until this hugely successful single was released. It made the band's second album, *Infest*, go triple platinum and they're now a serious force to be reckoned with.

How to play it

This riff features a three-fingered chord shape in four different positions on the fingerboard. For the first chord, place your first finger behind the 7th fret on the 5th string, your second finger behind the 9th fret on the 6th string and your third finger behind the 9th fret on the 4th string. Strum it twice.

Then move the whole shape down two frets so that your first finger is positioned at the 5th fret on the 5th string and play that twice. Move the shape down two more frets and play it again twice. Then move the shape down one more fret (your first finger now at the 2nd fret on 5th string) and play that twice. Finally, move the shape three frets back up the neck and play that twice before starting the riff again.

Guitar sound

The driving force behind Papa Roach's monster sound is guitarist Jerry Horton. He uses a signature model Schecter solidbody guitar with humbucking pickups and plays through a Marshall. His drop-tuning of the E string down to a low D also plays a part in the chunky sound of this and other Papa Roach riffs.

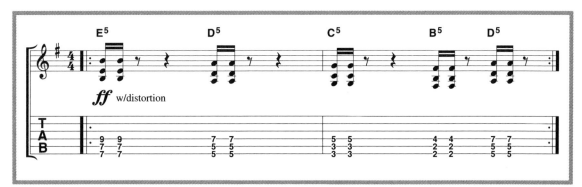

Words & Music by Papa Roach
© **Copyright 2000 Viva La Cucaracha Music/DreamWorks Songs, USA.**
Worldwide rights for Viva La Cucaracha Music and DreamWorks Songs administered by Cherry Lane Music
Publishing Company Incorporated, USA. All Rights Reserved. International Copyright Secured.

Linkin Park | Release date: April 2001 | Chart position: 16 | Album: *Hybrid Theory*

"I've always wanted our show to be energetic." Joseph Hahn

LINKIN PARK WERE ORIGINALLY called Hybrid Theory and they retained that name for the title of their debut album. The hybrid they were hinting at was that of rap and metal, and their music is a furious combination of the two.

How to play it

Although Linkin Park often use unusual tunings like C♯ G♯ C♯ F♯ A♯ D♯, the intro synth riff to 'Crawling' is easy to play with regular tuning as shown below. Position your fretting hand around the 11th – 14th frets to play this one comfortably.

Guitar sound

This intro riff works well with both clean and semi-distorted tones so play it with whatever amp settings you like. For most other Linkin Park parts, use a rock guitar (preferably with humbucker pickups) with the bridge pickup selected and loads of distortion!

Words & Music by Chester Bennington, Rob Bourdon, Brad Delson, Joseph Hahn & Mike Shinoda
© Copyright 2000 Zomba Songs Incorporated/Zomba Enterprises Incorporated, USA.
Zomba Music Publishers Limited. All Rights Reserved. International Copyright Secured.

44 Alive

P.O.D. | Release date: Sept 2001 | Album: *Satellite*

P.O.D., SHORT FOR "PAYABLE ON Death", are an unusual phenomenon: a born-again Christian Nü Metal band! Hailing from San Diego, they fuse the overdriven guitar sounds of grunge and metal with infectious hip-hop and reggae rhythms. Their debut single, 'Alive', was a big hit in the United States.

How to play it

To play this one, you'll need to tune your guitar strings down to C G D F A D (normal tuning dropped down a whole tone and with the lowest string dropped down even further to a low C).

Thanks to the tuning, this riff is as easy as they come! Flatten your first finger across the bottom three strings at the second fret, and simply move your hand around to play evil-sounding power chords on the open strings, and at the 2nd, 5th, 7th and 10th frets. Simple!

Guitar sound

Marcos Curiel, POD's guitarist for this recording, played a PRS guitar with Dragon II humbucking pickups. To get his

"We just wanna be as real as possible, you know, we're the same on stage as off." Sonny Sandoval

sound, use the bridge pickup, turn your volume and tone pots up full, and feed it into a rock amp with a medium amount of distortion.

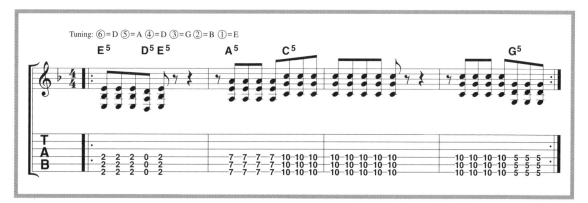

46 Flavor Of The Weak

American Hi-Fi | Release date: Sept 2001 | Chart position: 31 | Album: *American Hi-Fi*

'FLAVOR OF THE WEAK' WAS

American Hi-Fi's first hit single. Boasting catchy riffs and pop harmonies, it introduced a wider audience to the band's impressive self-named debut album. Their guitarist, Stacy Jones, used a dropped D tuning (normal tuning with the low E string tuned down to D) for this riff.

How to play it

Tune your 6th string down one tone to D – you can check the tuning with the open D string. Thanks to the tuning, the intro riff is as easy as they come! Hold one finger down flat across the 4th, 5th and 6th strings at the 5th, 3rd and 1st frets (see tab below).

You can create Stacy's 'chugging' sound by muting the strings slightly with the palm of your picking hand. The key to this riff is getting the right guitar sound (see below) and the rhythm. It's not complicated, but must be spot on – be sure not to catch extra strings, or let the chords ring on.

Guitar sound

American Hi-Fi use both Gibson and Fender guitars so you can use just about any solidbody electric for their music. Select the bridge pickup, turn the volume knob on your guitar up full, and crank in some overdrive on your amp.

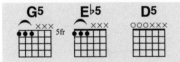

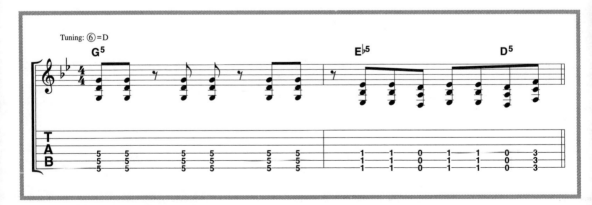

Words & Music by Stacy Jones
© Copyright 2001 Disciples of Judra/BMG Songs Incorporated, USA. BMG Music Publishing Limited.
All Rights Reserved. International Copyright Secured.

And I Love Her

The Beatles | Release date: July 1964 (album track) | Album: *A Hard Day's Night*

'AND I LOVE HER' IS A HAUNTING little ballad that dates back to the Beatles' *A Hard Day's Night* album. It is one of their most loved tunes, even though it was never released as a single or B-side!

How to play it

The most memorable part of this tune is the simple but effective four-note riff George Harrison played on an acoustic guitar.

To play it comfortably, position your fretting fingers over the first four frets at the end of the guitar neck. With your second finger, play the notes at the second frets on the fifth and fourth strings on the fingerboard. Then play the note at the first fret on the fourth string with your first finger and the note at the fourth fret on the fifth string with your little finger and hold it there until the end of the bar.

Guitar sound

You can play the notes straight like Harrison originally did or add a hint of vibrato on that last note. It can even be played on an electric instrument with a clean amp setting or, if you've got access to one, a subtle tremolo pedal effect.

"Written at Wimpole Street, it was the first ballad I impressed myself with."
Paul McCartney

50 Mrs Robinson

Simon & Garfunkel | Release date: July 1968 | Chart position: 4 | Album: *Bookends*

PAUL SIMON'S SONG 'MRS ROBINSON' was famously used by the film producer Mike Nicholls in his 1968 film, The Graduate. The original version of the song was actually called 'Mrs Roosevelt', but Nicholls persuaded Simon to change it to fit in with the film.

How to play it

The 'Mrs Robinson' intro section actually uses two guitars; one playing the little hammer-on riff below and the other strumming the bass strings of an E chord. Put a capo at the third fret. Then play the open sixth string, followed by the open fifth string and hammer down the second fret away from the capo with your second finger on the fifth string, and then the open fourth string followed by the second fret (not hammered) on that string. The second bar is very similar but there's another open sixth string note thrown in after the hammer-on.

Guitar sound

This tune would work well on a regular

"The job of a folk singer in those days was to be Bob Dylan. You had to be a poet. That's what they wanted and I thought that was a drag." Paul Simon

6-string acoustic or a 12-string guitar. Aim for an earthy, folky feel and make it sound as smooth and effortless as possible.

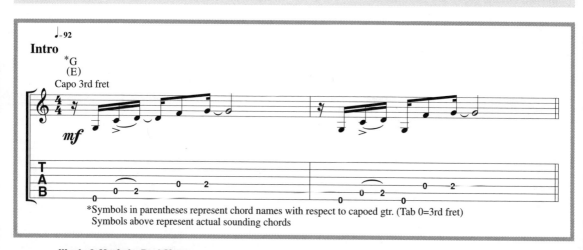

*Symbols in parentheses represent chord names with respect to capoed gtr. (Tab 0=3rd fret)
Symbols above represent actual sounding chords

52 All Along The Watchtower

Bob Dylan | Release date: March 1968 (album track) | Chart position: 5 (Hendrix version) | Album: *John Wesley Harding*

ALTHOUGH THIS SONG IS NORMALLY associated with Jimi Hendrix, it was actually written and recorded by Bob Dylan a year earlier for his low-key John Wesley Harding album. It has since been covered by many other rock and pop artists during the Seventies, Eighties and Nineties. For this example, we're going to play the intro to the Hendrix version on an acoustic guitar.

How to play it

Form a barred B major chord shape at the second fret (a B major chord) and play it twice. Then switch to the barred minor shape shown two frets further up (C♯ minor) and play that four times. Go back to your B major chord and play it twice again. Then play a regular A chord four times and repeat the whole sequence. These three chords form the basis of the whole song.

Guitar sound

You can use any guitar to strum the opening chords of this song. It works well both in a folk or a rock/pop context. If you're plugging into an amp, try using a fair amount of reverb to increase the depth of your sound – the more reverb, the bigger your sound!

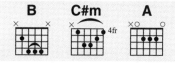

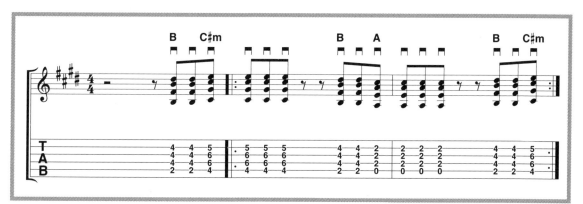

Words & Music by Bob Dylan
© Copyright 1968 Dwarf Music, USA.
All Rights Reserved. International Copyright Secured.

54 Wild Wood

Paul Weller | Release date: September 1993 | Chart position: 14 | Album: *Wild Wood*

HAILED AS PAUL WELLER'S FIRST masterwork since The Jam, 'Wild Wood' features a strong selection of folk and pop influenced songs including this catchy title track. We're going to look at how Paul plays its basic rhythm.

"All I wanted from the age of 12 was to be in a group."
Paul Weller

How to play it
Use a capo at the second fret. The riff is based around four chords, shown below. The strumming/picking pattern for the first two bars is shown in tab, so you could follow this for all eight bars, changing chord when appropriate.

Guitar sound
Weller's song can be played either on a steel-strung acoustic guitar or an electric instrument with clean amplification. If you're using an amp, use only the slightest hint of reverb or you'll end up swamping the sound.

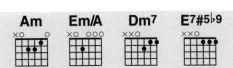

Am   Em/A   Dm7   E7#5♭9

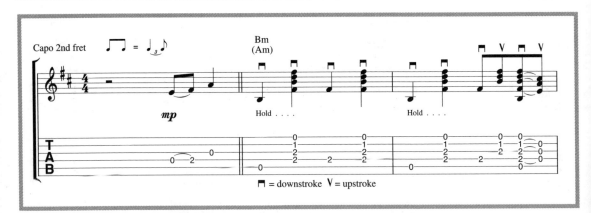

⊓ = downstroke V = upstroke

Wonderwall

Oasis | Release date: November 1995 | Chart position: 2 | Album: *(What's The Story) Morning Glory?*

THIS SONG WAS PENNED BY NOEL
Gallagher when his band of Brit Poppers were in their prime. It is one of a very small handful of chord progressions from the Nineties that can now be regarded as 'classic'.

How to play it

Use a capo at the second fret. First learn the chords in the progression: Em7, G, Dsus4 and A7sus4 (see below). When you can play these fluently, you can then focus on the strumming. Listen to the example on the CD and follow the notated strum patterns below (note that ⊓ is a downstroke and ∨ is an upstroke). Take it one chord at a time and then put them all together.

Guitar sound

Use a decent acoustic guitar with a nice action and medium gauge strings. The better the instrument you use for this, the sweeter it will sound, and the easier it will be to play! If you're playing it on an electric, choose a clean sound and add a little bit of reverb to bring it to life.

"I'm more of a strummer than a lead guitarist." Noel Gallagher

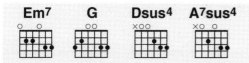

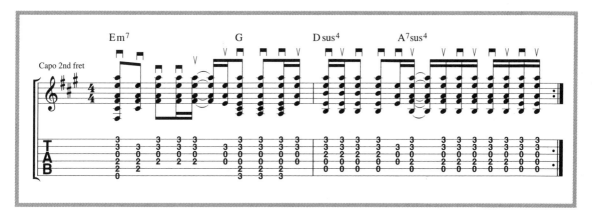

Why Does It Always Rain On Me?

Travis | Release date: August 1999 | Chart position: 10 | Album: *The Man Who*

THE RELEASE OF TRAVIS'S *THE MAN* *Who* album marked a switch from the band's previous murky pop sound to a quieter, more introspective style. It launched 'Why Does It Always Rain On Me?', a lilting singalong tune which took the UK charts by storm.

"The only thing you can do is give it one hundred per cent and hope that's good enough."
Fran Healy

How to play it

The intro for this song should be played by clamping a capo at the second fret and using traditional D, A minor and G shapes in their appropriate new positions in front of the capo to make the chords of the song: E, B minor and A. Extra colour can then be added to the A chord by taking your first and second fingers off the G shape and playing with your first finger on the note behind the second fret on the 6th string, and then on the note behind the second fret on the 5th string to make A/G# and F#m7 chords respectively. If you want to keep things really easy, however, just play the straight G shape for the last two bars.

Guitar sound

Use either an acoustic guitar or an electric or electro-acoustic going through a clean amp setting with some reverb. If you're using an amp, cut back a bit on the treble to obtain a warmer, mellower tone and try adding a touch of chorus.

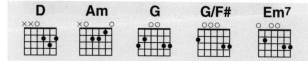

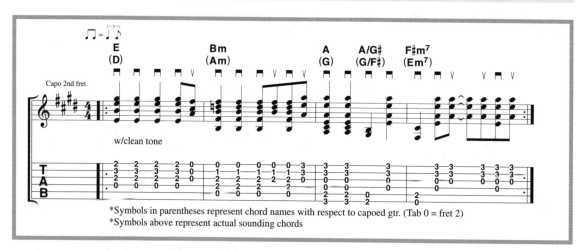

*Symbols in parentheses represent chord names with respect to capoed gtr. (Tab 0 = fret 2)
*Symbols above represent actual sounding chords

60 Yellow

Coldplay | Release date: June 2000 | Chart position: 4 | Album: *Parachutes*

COLDPLAY'S 'YELLOW' IS REGARDED BY many as being one of the first 'classic' songs of the 21st century. It features a very distinctive chord progression played by guitarist Chris Martin on a specially tuned acoustic guitar.

How to play it

To get a really authentic sound, you have to tune your guitar to E B D G B D♯, and play the chords at the 7th fret. However, to play along with the song, all you really need is two chords – B and Badd11. Basically, play a normal barre B major, and lift off the top E string to get B add11 (see the chord boxes below). The rhythm pattern is fairly simple too – all down strokes except for the last note in each bar.

Guitar sound

This tune works well with an 'unplugged' acoustic or one that is plugged into a suitable amp with a little bit of reverb and, if you have it, compression. Chris plays it on a Takamine EN-10 model guitar with a fitted piezo pickup.

"Johnny starts putting riffs on it, to make it better. That's what being in a band is all about." Chris Martin

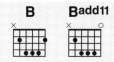

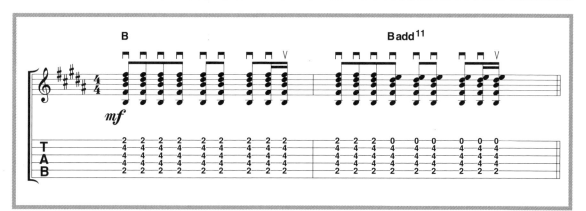

Words & Music by Guy Berryman, Jon Buckland, Will Champion & Chris Martin
© Copyright 2000 BMG Music Publishing Limited.
All Rights Reserved. International Copyright Secured.

62 Sail Away

David Gray | Release date: July 2001 | Chart position: 26 | Album: *White Ladder*

DAVID GRAY'S EMOTIVE VOICE AND songwriting skills have earned him critical respect over the past few years. He's also a great guitar player, using his acoustic instrument to create earthy voicings that complement his vocals. The catchy intro to 'Sail Away' only uses one Cm11 chord but it has a nice, dreamy quality.

How to play it

Put a capo behind the first fret to make sure you're playing in the same key as the CD track. Place your first finger of your fretting hand behind the 7th fret on the 3rd string, your third finger behind the 9th fret on the 5th string, and your little finger behind the 9th fret on the 4th string. Strum the chord as you hear it on the CD to the pattern below.

Guitar sound

This song works well on both 6- and 12-string guitars so either would do. If you have an electro-acoustic, you can enhance the tone further by plugging into an amp and using a soft chorus effect and some reverb.

Bm¹¹

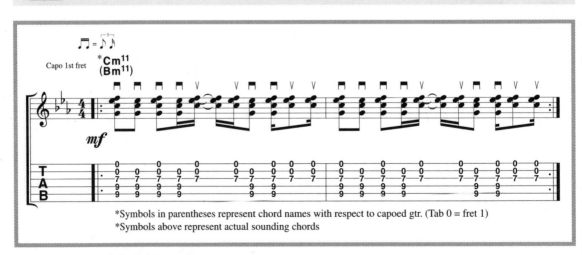

*Symbols in parentheses represent chord names with respect to capoed gtr. (Tab 0 = fret 1)
*Symbols above represent actual sounding chords

Jailhouse Rock

Elvis Presley | Release date: January 1958 | Chart position: 1
Album: *Elvis (Rock 'n' Roll No.1)*

IF YOU WERE ASKED TO THINK OF A
famous rock 'n' roll song, chances are that
this song or Bill Haley's 'Rock Around The
Clock' would be the first names to reach
your lips. 'Jailhouse Rock' owes a lot of its
drive and raunchiness to Scotty Moore,
Elvis' regular session and live guitarist.

How to play it
Start with riff A – a simple blues riff using
the open A string. Then play the riff in E,
followed by the riff in B. Now piece the
sections below together like this to get the
whole riff:

A A E E B A E E

This pattern makes up a basic blues which
has been used countless times over the
years in many different songs.

"It's hard to explain Rock'n'Roll.
It's not what you call folk music.
It's a beat that gets you. You feel it."
Elvis Presley

Guitar sound
A semi-acoustic guitar is ideal for obtaining
an authentic Fifties rock 'n' roll sound, but
you can also get it on a solidbody electric.
Select the bridge pickup and set your amp
to give a full-blooded tone by boosting
your mid-range a little. If you want some
icing on the cake, add a bit of slapback
echo set to around 100 milliseconds.

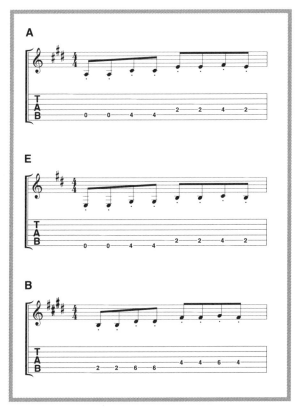

66 Not Fade Away

The Rolling Stones | Release date: February 1964 | Chart position: 3
Album: *The Rolling Stones*

IN THEIR EARLY YEARS, THE ROLLING
Stones covered many American songs
including this Buddy Holly classic. The
Stones, the Bluesbreakers and the Yardbirds
all played a role in introducing blues-
influenced music to a mainstream audience.

How to play it

This song uses three of the easiest chords
of all: E, A and D. You'll need to work a
little on the strumming, though. Strum all
six strings with alternating up and
downstrokes and use the palm of your
picking hand (or your fretting hand fingers)
to mute the strings after the chords to give
a more rhythmic effect. It might seem a
little awkward at first but take things slowly,
one step at a time, and you'll be surprised
at how easy it is to master.

Guitar sound

Although 'Not Fade Away' can certainly be

"Rock 'n' Roll is only any good
when you're confident about it."
Keith Richards

played on an acoustic guitar, an electric
instrument will sound more rock 'n' roll!
Use the bridge pickup and select a bright,
reverby tone on your amp.

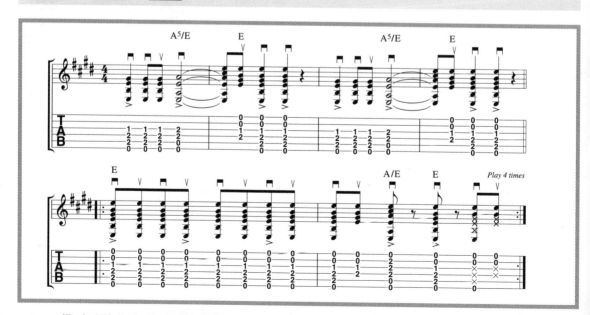

68 Dimples

John Lee Hooker | Release date: June 1964 | Chart position: 23
Album: *I'm John Lee Hooker*

THIS LEGENDARY BLUESMAN
propelled his cool boogie songs with a
relentless foot tapping. His impressive
career stretched over more than half a
century and his many fans include Eric
Clapton and B.B. King.

How to play it

Although this intro sounds like a typical
lead guitar riff, only one finger is actually
used to play it: your first finger. Play the
note behind the second fret on the third
string and bend it up quickly so that it
sounds the same pitch as the note behind
the third fret, and back down again. Do
this up/down bend smoothly, as if it is
being executed in one action.

Now play the open third string and then
the note behind the second fret, followed by
the open string again. Next play the second
fret note on the fourth string, then a pull-
off to the open fourth string, and then the
second fret note on the fourth string again.
This phrase can be played through an
entire 12-bar blues progression!

"You know, I feel like I'm the father of
a whole lot of people." John Lee Hooker

Guitar sound

John Lee Hooker is usually associated with
semi-acoustic guitars and, indeed, you'll
need a semi-acoustic such as a Gibson 335
or an Epiphone model to get a truly
authentic tone. Nevertheless, you can
approximate to Hooker's sound with any
solidbody equipped with humbuckers: use
the bridge pickup and go through an amp
with the mid and treble cut back a little.
And don't forget the sunglasses if you want
to look the part!

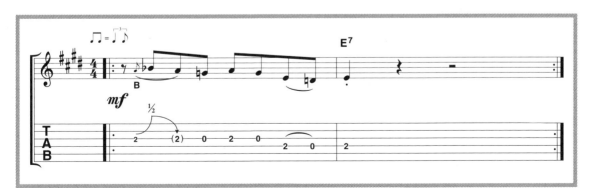

Words & Music by James Bracken & John Lee Hooker
© Copyright 1956 & 1968 Conrad Music/Arc Music Corporation, USA. Tristan Music Limited.
All Rights Reserved. International Copyright Secured.

The Beatles | Release date: April 1965 | Chart position: 1 | Album/film: *Help!*

THIS SONG REPRESENTS ONE of the Beatles' earliest forays into the world of psychedelic rock. Both John Lennon and George Harrison played Rickenbacker 12-string electrics on it to get a 'jangly' sound which is usualy associated with the Byrds.

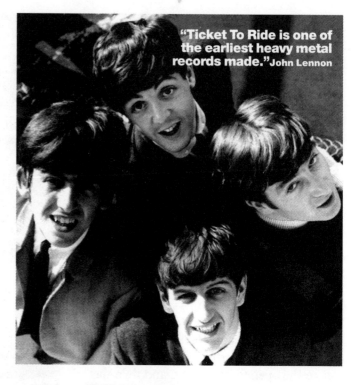

"Ticket To Ride is one of the earliest heavy metal records made." John Lennon

How to play it

The instantly recognisable riff which introduces this song is played on the first three guitar strings with a plectrum. All of the notes except for the B (second note from the end) can be played as part of a held down A chord. To get the B note, simply take your fretting finger away from the second fret of the second string to let the open string ring out.

Watch out for the triplet at the end of the bar. It features three quarter (crotchet) notes to be fitted into the time of two, which gives it a slightly unsettled, off-beat feel. Listen carefully to the CD to make sure you're getting it right.

Guitar sound

A 12-string Rickenbacker, as used by the guys originally, would certainly be ideal for this song but you can also get a similar effect by playing a 6-string electric through an amp with some extra treble and a subtle short delay effect (to simulate the sound of a 12-string). A little bit of reverb would also do nicely.

Day Tripper

The Beatles | Release date: December 1965 | Chart position: 1
Album: *The Beatles: 1962-1966*

ALTHOUGH MOST OF THE BEATLES' songs were built around chord progressions, a few of their tunes were riff-led. 'Day Tripper' is based around a simple riff played in the key of E.

How to play it

The 'Day Tripper' riff uses notes from the fourth, fifth and sixth strings. Position your fretting hand around the first few frets at the end of the neck and play an open sixth string, followed by the notes at the third and fourth frets on that same string. Next play the notes behind the second frets on the fifth and fourth strings, followed by the open fourth string.

Then, for the next bar play the note behind the second fret on the fifth string, followed by the fourth fret on the fourth string, the second fret on the fifth string, the open fourth string, and, finally, the second fret on the fourth string. Then go back and repeat the riff again. And again. And again.

Guitar sound

Both Lennon and Harrison were using semi-solid guitars to get that twangy sound, so a similar guitar such as a Gibson 335 or Rickenbacker would be perfect. However, you can obtain a similar sound on a solidbody electric with the bridge pickup selected, the mid range control on your amp boosted a little, and a splash of reverb.

"We were just getting better technically and musically, that's all." John Lennon

74 Lucy In The Sky With Diamonds

The Beatles | Release date: June 1967 (album track)
Album: *Sgt. Pepper's Lonely Hearts Club Band*

THERE ARE SEVERAL STANDOUT
tracks from Sgt Pepper, the best-selling
album of all time in the UK, but this
psychedelic song could well be the most
popular. 'Lucy In The Sky With
Diamonds' is said either to have been
named after the drug LSD, or from a
drawing by John's son Julian. It starts
with a haunting riff in 3/4 time.

How to play it
Position your fretting hand around the
9th to 12th frets and play the notes as
shown below on the first, second and
third strings. The last bar features a
pull-off from the 10th fret to the 9th fret
on the first string. This is obtained by
placing your first finger behind the 9th
fret on that string, using your second finger
to play the note at the 10th fret (with your
first finger still holding down the 9th fret)
and then pulling your second finger off the
fingerboard to let the note at the 9th fret
ring out.

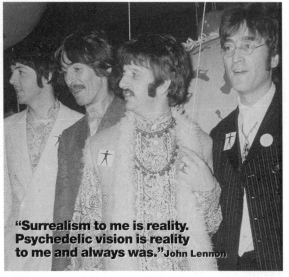

"Surrealism to me is reality.
Psychedelic vision is reality
to me and always was." John Lennon

Guitar sound
The original Beatles intro riff was actually
played on a keyboard but it would also
work well with an electric guitar. To make
it sound as psychedelic as possible, try
putting it through a chorus, phaser or
flanger pedal and let the notes ring out.

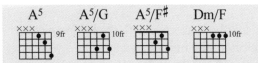

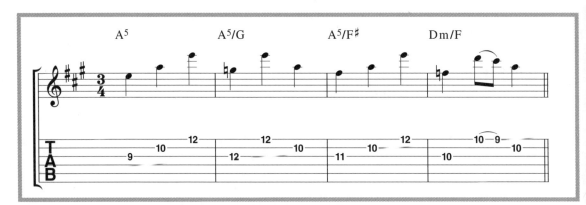

David Bowie | Release date: October 1977 | Chart position: 24 | Album: *Heroes*

DAVID BOWIE HAS WRITTEN MANY famous riffs over the years but this is one of the easiest to play. It features an insistent, repetitive rhythm strengthened by some ethereal electric guitar work.

How to play it

The riff starts with the first and third fingers on the fourth and fifth strings and moves to the outer two strings. The fourth bar has a phrase using all of the notes between the second and fifth frets (a chromatic phrase) on the fifth string. As will all new pieces of music, take it slowly at first and then play it faster when you know it off by heart.

Guitar sound

The original rhythm guitar on 'Heroes' was played by session musician Carlos Alomar, although the legendary Robert Fripp also played some great lead lines on it. Use a solidbody electric and play through a rock amp with a medium amount of distortion.

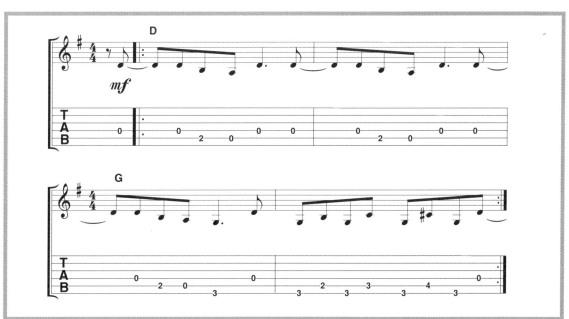

Wonderful Tonight

Eric Clapton | Release date: November 1977 | Chart position: 30 (1991 live version)
Album: *Slowhand*

WONDERFUL TONIGHT' FIRST
appeared on Eric Clapton's legendary
album Slowhand in 1977, although it was
also released more than a decade later as a
live single. Due to its slow speed, and
simple melody, it's pretty easy to play.

How to play it
Use the third finger of your fretting hand
to finger the first note at the 10th fret on
the 2nd string. Bend the note up a whole
tone (so that it sounds like the note you'd
hear at the 12th fret on the same string)
and smoothly ease the bend down again so
that the up/down bend is continuous. Play
the note at the 8th fret on the same string
with your first finger, and then the note at
the 10th fret again with your third finger.
That's the basis of the riff. Watch out for
the slides in bar 8!

Guitar sound
Eric usually performs this song on a
Stratocaster, but you can play it on almost
any electric solidbody instrument you like.
Light to medium gauge strings will make

"The best track
from Slowhand
has got to be
'Wonderful Tonight',
because the
song is nice."
Eric Clapton

the string bends nice and easy. Use a
reasonably clean tone, with just a hint of
distortion, and play it loud enough to let
those notes sustain long enough.

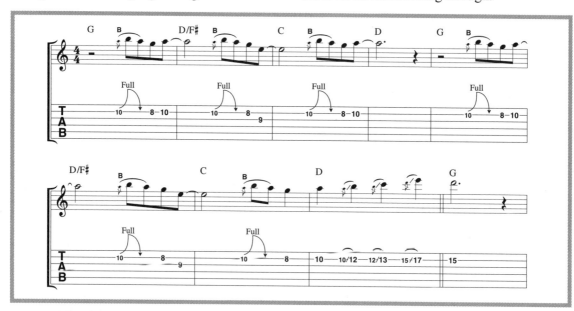

Sultans Of Swing

Dire Straits | Release date: March 1979 | Chart position: 8 | Album: *Dire Straits*

THIS LEGENDARY DIRE STRAITS SONG was an unlikely hit back in 1979, but now it is regarded as a guitar shop 'classic'. Based on the story of a jazz pub band, the song features chord progressions and guitar licks that are instantly recognisable.

How to play it

'Sultans Of Swing' features lots of rhythm guitar parts including the chord progression used to start off each of the verses: Dm, C, B♭, A.

You can play these chords straight or with extra rhythm strokes. An F chord is also used later on in the verses. Alternatively, we've tabbed out the chorus riff below.

'Sultans Of Swing' is also a great tune to jam to as you can solo over most of the song using only one scale, the D natural minor scale, shown right (5th fret position).

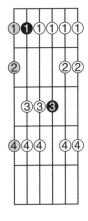

Guitar sound

Mark Knopfler originally recorded this song with a Fender Strat but you can play this rhythm part on just about any electric guitar. Use a clean sound with a dash of chorus and delay to spice it up a little bit.

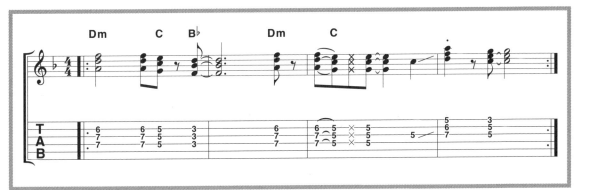

82 Gimme Some Lovin'

Blues Brothers | Release date: 1980 (Album track)
Album: *The Blues Brothers (soundtrack)*

THE BLUES BROTHERS started out as an R&B spoof on the NBC television sketch comedy series Saturday Night Live, but they developed into a surprisingly good live act who introduced blues and soul classics to a whole new generation of listeners. Their version of 'Gimme Some Lovin'' begins with a simple but extremely catchy riff.

How to play it

Play the open fourth string once and then the note behind the second fret on that string four times with your first finger. Then play the open sixth string and repeat the phrase again and again. Use all downstrokes as this will make the riff sound more powerful!

Guitar sound

The Blues Brothers used some of the best Memphis session men around at the time including ex-Booker T and the MGs guitarist Steve Cropper. Steve often played a Fender Telecaster to get a biting tone that could cut right through a mix. Use your bridge pickup through an amp with just a bit of distortion and, if necessary, some extra treble.

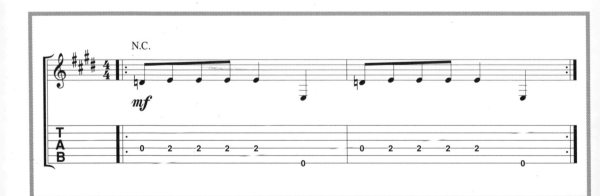

Addicted To Love

Robert Palmer | Release date: May 1986 | Chart position: 5 | Album: *Riptide*

ALTHOUGH MUCH OF THIS SINGLE'S success can be accredited to Palmer's use of leggy models as his video backing band, it also boasted a superb production and a great blues-style riff.

How to play it
Most of this riff is played using two note chords (or 'double stops') as shown below. The main focus is on the 5th and 6th strings, except for the D5 chord where the 4th and 5th strings are used.

Guitar sound
The 'Addicted To Love' riff has a powerful, biting sound. You can get this sort of tone by playing a Telecaster or Stratocaster style guitar through a rock amp with plenty of gain. If you're using a guitar with

humbucking pickups, you might want to adjust your instrument's or amp's tone controls to get a more biting sound.

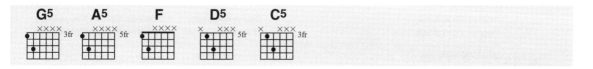

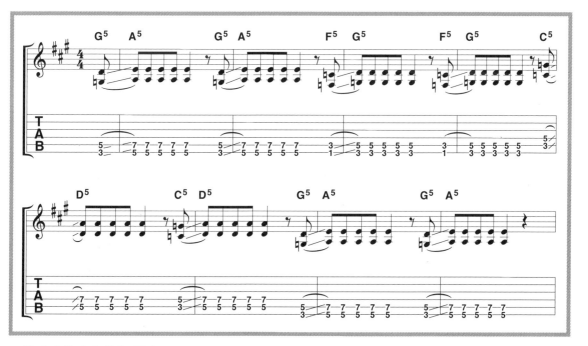

Track No.		Track title	Artist
1	**Tuning Notes**		
2-3	**All Day And All Of The Night** **All Day And All Of The Night**	**Slow version** **Backing track**	**The Kinks** **The Kinks**
4-5	**Sunshine Of Your Love** **Sunshine Of Your Love**	**Slow version** **Backing track**	**Eric Clapton** **Eric Clapton**
6-7	**Oye Como Va** **Oye Como Va**	**Slow version** **Backing track**	**Santana** **Santana**
8-9	**Pretty Vacant** **Pretty Vacant**	**Slow version** **Backing track**	**Sex Pistols** **Sex Pistols**
10-11	**Run To You** **Run To You**	**Slow version** **Backing track**	**Bryan Adams** **Bryan Adams**
12-13	**Livin' On A Prayer** **Livin' On A Prayer**	**Slow version** **Backing track**	**Bon Jovi** **Bon Jovi**
14-15	**There She Goes** **There She Goes**	**Slow version** **Backing track**	**The Las** **The Las**
16-17	**Fools Gold** **Fools Gold**	**Slow version** **Backing track**	**The Stone Roses** **The Stone Roses**
18-19	**The Day We Caught The Train** **The Day We Caught The Train**	**Slow version** **Backing track**	**Ocean Colour Scene** **Ocean Colour Scene**
20-21	**Road Rage** **Road Rage**	**Slow version** **Backing track**	**Catatonia** **Catatonia**
22-23	**Found That Soul** **Found That Soul**	**Slow version** **Backing track**	**Manic Street Preachers** **Manic Street Preachers**
24-25	**Burn Baby Burn** **Burn Baby Burn**	**Slow version** **Backing track**	**Ash** **Ash**
26-27	**Just A Day** **Just A Day**	**Slow version** **Backing track**	**Feeder** **Feeder**
28-29	**Paranoid** **Paranoid**	**Slow version** **Backing track**	**Black Sabbath** **Black Sabbath**
30-31	**Highway To Hell** **Highway To Hell**	**Slow version** **Backing track**	**AC/DC** **AC/DC**
32-33	**Bring Your Daughter... To The Slaughter** **Bring Your Daughter... To The Slaughter**	**Slow version** **Backing track**	**Iron Maiden** **Iron Maiden**
34-35	**Enter Sandman** **Enter Sandman**	**Slow version** **Backing track**	**Metallica** **Metallica**
36-37	**Falling Away From Me** **Falling Away From Me**	**Slow version** **Backing track**	**Korn** **Korn**
38-39	**Buck Rogers** **Buck Rogers**	**Slow version** **Backing track**	**Feeder** **Feeder**
40-41	**Last Resort** **Last Resort**	**Slow version** **Backing track**	**Papa Roach** **Papa Roach**
42-43	**Crawling** **Crawling**	**Slow version** **Backing track**	**Linkin Park** **Linkin Park**

5/04 (51104)